The Meat Free Fitness Menu

51 Healthy Vegetarian Recipes For Gym Lovers

Marc McLean & Victoria Murphy

Table of Contents

Introduction

Remember those days when everyone thought steak and protein shakes were the only route to a strong, lean body?

"How can a vegetarian hope to build muscle?" the gym meatheads said.

"Those vegans aren't getting in enough nutrients," they claimed.

Those days are like the Dark Ages now as many thousands of people across the world have proven that meat-free is the way to go for a leaner, stronger, *healthier* body.

And science is now clearly showing that athletes are improving their performance, building their strength, extending their endurance, and boosting their health by following a plant-based diet.

The same benefits can be experienced by gym lovers like you, me, and other men and women trying to get in amazing shape.

- But what foods should you be eating while following a gym programme?

- What meals should you be having post-workout?

- How much protein is needed to develop lean muscle and keep bodyfat levels low...and what about carbs, and the best fat sources?

Just some of the questions you may be asking right now. Then again, I've found that the people who have given up meat are generally more clued-up about nutrition and health than the average Joe...or Josephine.

Wouldn't it be easier if you had a big collection of healthy vegetarian recipes – ones that are perfect for gym lovers trying to get in great shape – all compiled in one book?

Wouldn't it be easier if you could choose from a wide selection of meat-free main meals, breakfasts, superfood shakes and healthy snacks?

Wouldn't your meat-free life be complete if the recipes were tasty, simple to make...and there was a complete nutritional breakdown provided for every one of them? (So, no need to worry about how many calories, grams of protein, carbs or fat you're having).

Well, your best buds Marc McLean and Victoria Murphy are about to make all that happen with *The Meat Free Fitness Menu*.

I'm Marc, an online personal trainer, author of the Strength Training 101 book series, and owner of Weight Training Is The Way.

My books have reached more than 20,000 readers all over the world in a couple of years, helping men and women build strong, lean, athletic bodies...in the healthiest way possible.

That means challenging weight training workouts in the gym that you love, backed up with natural, plant-based nutrition for health and wellbeing.

Victoria is my partner – and partner in crime when it comes to exercise and nutrition. We're both 37 years old and are in better shape now than we were in our 20s.

We finally realised why: it's all down to our diet.

Sure, we hit the gym. But we usually only go three times per week. It doesn't matter how hard you train if you're putting the wrong kind of fuel in the tank.

That doesn't mean we're about to tell you to be super strict with your nutrition, ban loads of foods, or follow an eating plan that you'll hate.

No, it's all about being clever with your diet and replacing the crap (i.e. meat that clogs up your arteries and increases your risk of various diseases) with super tasty alternatives.

Here's a quick example: about 10 years ago I switched from dairy-based whey protein powders because they were messing with my gut, and I'd also learned many of them were filled with all sorts of sweeteners, additives, and unnatural e-numbers.

Back then, I thought the only alternative was hemp protein powder. Have you ever tried one of those shakes? It's like drinking mud - with a slight flavouring of sweat and peanuts!

Then I discovered super tasty plant-based protein powders, made from the likes of pea protein and brown rice protein. These came in great flavours, but then I also started mixing in berries as a great carbs source and for their antioxidants. Next, I'd throw almonds or seeds into the mix for healthy fats, and ground ginger to give the shake a tasty kick — with the added anti-inflammatory benefits.

Suddenly I'd gone from unhealthy protein shakes damaging my guts and an alternative that tasted like mucky, sweaty feet...to a ridiculously tasty, superfood shake that was jam-packed with more nutrients than most people get in an entire day!

Victoria and I have experimented with lots of nutritious shake recipes, meals, and healthy snacks that can help us achieve our fitness goals — and maintain good health.

We quickly realised that vastly reducing/eliminating meat food sources from our diet was the way to do this. When we did, we felt better, looked better, had more energy, and our performance in the gym improved.

As well as coming up with plenty of our own recipes, we've spent years hunting down healthy meat-free dishes on TV, in cookery books, in articles and online.

We've compiled the best of the best – or tastiest of the tastiest – for you in *The Meat Free Fitness Menu*. Every recipe is simple to make and many of them are ready in 2 mins-25 mins. We know the last thing you want to do before or after a workout is spend ages preparing and cooking a complicated meal.

Also, we've broken the recipes down into 4 straightforward sections so that you can quickly dive in and find what you want to make without messing around. Those sections are: breakfast and superfood smoothies; healthy snacks; macro meals (low or high calorie); and post-workout meals.

We've also provided a nutritional breakdown for every single recipe...so you know exactly how many calories are in each one, along with how many grams of protein, carbs and fat.

It took us roughly 87,032 hours to do accurate calculations for every recipe. But that's okay...it's cos we love you.

We've also thrown in a bonus chapter from Marc's top-selling book *Strength Training Nutrition 101: Build Muscle & Burn Fast Easily...A Healthy Way Of Eating You Can Actually Maintain*.

The chapter is titled 'Do We Really Need ALL That Protein?', and delves into why many fitness fanatics are getting it wrong when it comes to levels of protein and other macronutrients in their diet.

Maintaining a healthy diet can be hard, especially when you run out of good food ideas. All of that is about to change for you...

This book is packed with 51 delicious, zero meat recipes that you're going to love, and will help you build a lean, strong, healthy body.

Don't hang around. We've served up *The Meat Free Fitness Menu*...it's now up you to make your selections so you can take your health and fitness to the next level.

A Game Changer For Your Health & Fitness

I was just minding my business one day in October 2019 when my mobile phone started blowing up.

Well, it didn't exactly blow up. That would've been disappointing.

I'm talking about a tornado of text messages I wasn't expecting. The first one read: "Marc, have you seen the documentary on Netflix called Game Changers?"

Quickly followed by: "It's brilliant...definitely right up your street!"

Then another message from my friend James. "Have you watched Game Changers yet?"

I hadn't seen, or knew anything about this documentary. But I was already pretty sure it was about health and fitness. That's because the messages were coming in from my former personal training clients; people who used to eat high amounts of meat and animal products before I started coaching them.

I had advised them to reduce the amount of meat in their diet, find some plant-based alternatives, and ditch their usual whey protein shakes for a Vegan blend.

Now I've got a quick confession to make: I am NOT a vegetarian or a vegan. I also don't like to preach about one diet being better than the other. Each to their own, and all that.

What I am is someone extremely interested in sports nutrition, the workings of the body, and how to maintain good health and wellbeing. I've studied diet and nutrition for over a decade now, not simply because I lift weights at the gym and want to be in good physical shape.

It's mainly because I've experienced health issues over the years, and quickly understood that diet and nutrition is critical to both regaining, and maintaining, overall health.

Ever since the day the doctor told me I had IBS and would have to take pills for the rest of my life, I knew I had to figure out another way. Plus, I was supposed to be the fit and healthy guy who never missed the gym. How the hell did I end up with a dodgy digestive system and a load of pills for eternity?

After countless hours of reading numerous books, scientific studies, articles, taking courses, and watching videos online, it became pretty obvious that too much meat was bad news for your overall health.

Scientists had found direct links between long term meat consumption, and too many animal products overall, with major diseases including stroke, type II diabetes and diseases of the kidneys, heart and liver.

Too much meat causes an inflammatory response in the body - and chronic inflammation is at the root of most disease. Depending on various factors, such as increased stress levels or simply your genetic make-up, your body can have a seriously hard time digesting meat too.

When you consider that most meat products contains hormones and antibiotics, over-consumption can leave a sickening soup of toxins floating around in your body.

This can cause havoc with your digestive system, your endocrine system, and wipe out your all-important good gut bacteria. And since 80% of our immune system is located in our gut, and is directly connected to our brain function, it's easy to see how what we put in our mouths affects our overall health.

I'm guessing most readers who have picked up this book will be clued-up on all of this information anyway. You probably made the choice to go meat free in order to protect your health, and/or due to animal cruelty reasons.

My point is that my health improved big time when I drastically reduced my meat intake and adopted a better diet overall. (Admittedly, I still eat chicken occasionally but only once or twice per week now compared to every day previously).

I didn't need the doctor's pills after all. Years later, my digestive health took another nosedive after the stress of my dad dying and my diet slipping for a while. I was diagnosed with severe ulcerative colitis – for which there is no cure apparently – but I managed to reverse it completely by resuming my previous clean diet and an alternative health technique called the Wim Hof Method.

That's why my partner Victoria and I have followed an (almost) meat free diet for years to support our fitness and stay as healthy as possible. It's also why I've always told my fitness clients that reducing their overall meat intake and replacing it with more plant-based foods is a smart move for their health.

I have the same advice for everyone: "You don't have to eat meat to build muscle and get in great shape.

"There's no point trying to look lean and strong on the outside, when your body's on fire and on the way to disease on the inside."

Two years ago, I published my first recipe book *Meal Prep: 50 Simple Recipes For Health & Fitness Nuts*. It includes a wide variety of healthy meals for people on a non-restrictive diet, and I've had great feedback from readers who love the recipes.

Problem is, I don't eat many of the dishes I included in that book these days. We generally cut out meat Monday-Friday in our house, instead eating the tasty foods you're about to discover on the following pages. At the weekend, we'll relax our diet and have a Chinese takeaway, which will include chicken, and occasionally some smoked bacon and eggs on a Sunday.

This might be a complete no-no for hardcore vegetarians and I understand that. Personally, I think it's all about balance - and doing what's best most of the time. I also stress to personal training clients that there's a big misconception that you must eat lots of protein to reach your fitness goals.

In my book *Strength Training Nutrition 101*, I go into much more detail on protein requirements for people who regularly train at the gym, and want to develop lean muscle and keep bodyfat levels low. Remember, I've included that particular chapter as a bonus for you at the end of this book.

For now, let's see what's on The Meat Free Fitness Menu...

Breakfasts and Superfood Smoothies

It feels like we're lying to you.

That's because we've called this chapter 'Breakfasts and Superfood Smoothies'...yet we only eat breakfast once or twice per week.

It's all down to intermittent fasting. We've been following intermittent fasting for years now, which basically involves delaying breakfast and eating a few hours later instead.

It's easily one of the most effective tactics we use to keep bodyfat levels low, while maintaining muscle, and eating this way has numerous health benefits including:

- Burning fat on autopilot
- Slowing aging
- Protecting against brain disorders
- Helping prevent killer diseases included diabetes and cancer
- Improving heart health

We won't keep banging on about intermittent fasting as this is covered in much more detail in Marc's books *Fitness Hacking* and *Burn Fat Fast*....and, erm, also because this is supposed to be a recipe book.

But we're just giving you a quick heads-up on intermittent fasting as it's a much better option for staying healthy and lean than any fad diet you may have tried in the past.

In the following pages, we've listed 12 dishes and smoothies that are ideal for your first meal of the day. Whether you have these at breakfast, mid-morning, or lunchtime, they are all tasty

11

nutritious meals you're gonna love.

What's On The Menu

Poached Eggs & Avocado On Toast

Berry Bowl Breakfast

Protein Waffles

Blueberry Pancakes

Almond & Fruit Brekkie Mix

Veggie Scrambled Eggs

Mango & Pineapple Yoghurt

Banana & Mango Smoothie

Chocolate & Blueberry Smoothie

Super Green Smoothie

Blueberry Chia Smoothie

Banana & Berry Smoothie

Superfood Smoothies

Having a shake as your first meal of the day is a really smart move for three reasons:

1) It's easier on your digestive system and won't leave you feeling heavy.

2) It's convenient: no need for cooking, simply take a shaker bottle with you to work.

3) It's packed with more vitamins and minerals than most people have in a day.

The shake recipes we describe in the following pages are simple: put all the listed ingredients in a blender and whizz it all together. One minute later and you've got a superfood meal.

Our shake recipes follow the same simple formula:

- **Each shake contains a scoop of non-dairy based protein powder** as whey protein is often very acidic and harder to digest. We opt for the 'Vegan Blend' protein powder, which comes in various flavours and is available for a reasonable price at www.myprotein.com.

The Vegan Blend range is made with protein powder is made with pea protein and fava bean isolate, and 1 scoop serving provides 22g-23g of highly absorbable protein. It's also made with a natural sweetener, steviol glycosides, and doesn't contain any dodgy e-number ingredients or unhealthy additives.

- **Fruits as a good source of carbs**, vitamins and, in the case of blueberries, a brilliant source of antioxidants.

- **Nuts or seeds** are a top ingredient because they're a great source of healthy fats and protein. (Excluding peanuts as they are a very high source of lectins, a type of protein that causes inflammation in the body).

- **Greens...and they've got to be organic**. Don't be cheap when it comes to your health; spend a little more to grab the bag of spinach that's not been sprayed with pesticides and harmful chemicals.

- **Spices** such as ground ginger and cinnamon are always included. Both of these are anti-inflammatory foods — and shakes don't taste nearly as good without them. By cutting out meat and adding anti-inflammatory foods to your diet, you'll assist your body in recovering from workouts and strengthening your immune system.

Okay, let's get stuck into the first meal of the day.

Almond & Fruit Brekkie Mix

(Ready in 3-4 mins)

We were being a wee bit conservative saying above that this is ready to serve in 3-4 mins. You might well be able to do it in 30-40 secs.

Fancy trying a world record attempt? We'll time you. Ready, set, go...

Ingredients

2 tbsp of flaxseed

¼ tsp of turmeric

1 tsp ground ginger

Handful of organic kale

1 cup of raspberries

1 frozen ripe banana

1 cup almond milk

1 tbsp of almond butter

1 tbsp of Greek yoghurt

1 tbsp of granola

Servings: 1

Nutrition Per Serving

Calories: 533

Protein: 20g

Carbs: 64g

Fat: 26g

Serving Instructions

Step 1

Add the flaxseed, turmeric, ground ginger, organic kale, frozen banana and almond milk to a blender. Whizz for 1 minute until smooth.

Step 2

Pour the mixture into a bowl and then add a layer of granola, a dollop of almond butter, a tbsp of Greek yoghurt, and raspberries on top.

Blueberry Pancakes

(Ready in 15 mins)

Who doesn't like blueberries? And if you don't like pancakes then you've gotta have a serious word with yourself!

Combine the two in this awesome recipe – and you've got a breakfast of brilliance.

Ingredients

1 ½ cups fresh blueberries

2 tbsp maple syrup

1 tsp lemon juice

½ tsp ground cinnamon

¾ cup wholewheat flour

1 tsp Stevia sweetener powder

1 teaspoon baking powder

¼ teaspoon salt

½ cup almond milk

1 egg

1 ½ tbsp coconut oil

Servings – 4

Nutrition Per Serving

Calories: 178

Protein: 5g

Carbs: 33g

Fat: 4g

Cooking instructions

Step 1

Place a small saucepan over a low-medium heat, and add in 1

cup (170g) of the blueberries, along with the syrup, cinnamon and lemon juice. Cook for 4-5 mins until the blueberries have popped and released their juices. Stir regularly to ensure all ingredients are well mixed, remove from heat, and keep aside for later.

Step 2

Using a large bowl, whisk together the wholewheat flour, Stevia sweetener, salt and baking powder.

Step 3

Heat the coconut oil in a small saucepan until melted. Add the coconut oil liquid to a bowl, along with the almond milk and egg, and whisk together.

Step 4

Pour the coconut, almond milk and egg mix into the large bowl with the dry ingredients. Add the remaining blueberries and stir well until everything is combined in a batter consistency.

Step 5

Mist a non-stick pan with cooking spray and heat at medium for 1-2 mins. Scoop the batter into a ¼ cup measure and pour into the pan. Repeat and cook 3-4 small pancakes in the pan at once.

Step 6

Flip the pancakes after 2-3 minutes once the edges begin to dry. Cook on the second side until cooked through. Serve with the blueberry syrup made at the beginning.

Poached Eggs & Avocado On Toast

(Ready in 10-12 mins)

Eggs and avocado? Two super sources of healthy fats and protein.

Throw some wholegrain bread and baby tomatoes into the mix for your carbohydrates, and you've got an all-round, well-balanced brekkie.

Ingredients

2 large free range eggs

2 slices of whole grain bread

½ small avocado

1 tbsp of shaved parmesan cheese

½ tsp of dried thyme

Handful of baby tomatoes, quartered

Salt and pepper

Servings – 1

Nutrition Per Serving

Calories: 507

Protein: 26g

Carbs: 44g

Fat: 25g

Cooking Instructions

Step 1

Half fill a wide saucepan with water, add a dash of salt, and bring it to the boil. Drop the metal rims of two mason jars into the bottom of the saucepan so that they are lying flat on the bottom.

Step 2

After the water reaches boiling point, reduce the heat to a simmer and then carefully crack the eggs into each rim.

Step 3

Cover the pot with a lid and poach the eggs for 5 mins.

Step 4

Toast the bread while the eggs are cooking, and then mash up ½ an avocado and spread onto each slice of bread.

Step 5

Gently remove the eggs from the lids and saucepan, and place them onto the toast. Sprinkle with Parmesan cheese, salt, pepper, and ½ tsp of dried thyme.

Mango-Pineapple Yoghurt Bowl

(Ready in 5-6 mins)

Some fruity, yoghurt-y magic to get your day off to a great, healthy start.

This is another simple recipe that you could whip up quickly in the morning.

Ingredients

1 tbsp coconut flakes

1 cup (250 grams) Greek yoghurt

¼ cup diced fresh pineapple chunks

¼ cup diced fresh mango chunks

2 tbsp walnut pieces, chopped

1 tsp chia seeds

Servings – 1

Nutrition Per Serving

Calories: 470

Protein: 30g

Carbs: 49g

Fat: 18g

Cooking instructions

Step 1

Scoop half the yoghurt into a deep cereal bowl, and mix in the mango and pineapple chunks.

Step 2

Toast the coconut flakes over medium-high heat in a non-stick pan until golden brown.

Step 3

Scatter the coconut flakes over the yoghurt and fruit, then add the remaining yoghurt as another layer.

Step 4

Top with the walnuts and chia seeds, and then serve.

Protein Waffles

(Ready in 10 mins)

No, not the potato waffles covered with baked beans we got for dinner as kids. We're talking some seriously tasty protein waffles made with all-natural, healthy ingredients...eggs, flaxseed, cinnamon, honey.

Okay, we'll stop waffling on. Enjoy!

Ingredients

1 scoop chocolate protein powder

2 large free-range eggs

2 tbsp ground flaxseed/linseed

2 tbsp almond, coconut or oat flour

75ml almond milk

1 tsp ground cinnamon

1 tsp honey

Servings – 1

Nutrition Per Serving

Calories: 470

Protein: 40g

Carbs: 12g

Fat: 26g

Cooking instructions

Step 1

Turn on waffle maker and, once it heats up, spray with a little non-stick spray.

Step 2

Using a food processor (or handheld blender and large mixing bowl), blend all of the above ingredients together to create a thick batter.

Step 3

Pour the waffle mix onto the waffle maker and close until waffles are cooked.

Drizzle with honey with honey. (* Also great with a dollop of Greek yoghurt and blueberries if you're feeling a bit adventurous).

Berry Bowl Breakfast

(Ready in 1-2 mins)

Simple. Sweet. Stupidly delicious.

Ingredients

200g plain Greek yoghurt

Handful of blueberries

4 strawberries, quartered

2 tbsp of granola

½ tbsp of linseed/flaxseed

1 tbsp of almond butter

½ tsp of ground ginger

Servings – 1

Nutrition Per Serving

Calories: 528

Protein: 28g

Carbs: 48g

Fat: 26g

Serving Instructions

Step 1

Scoop yoghurt into a large bowl, add ½ tsp of ground ginger, and mix it up.

Step 2

Add the remaining ingredients in any wacky order you choose.

Step 3

Get stuck right into that bowl of dreams.

Veggie Scrambled Eggs On Toast

(Ready in 10-12 mins)

You can't beat a bit of egg scrambling, especially when you get all these other healthy veggies involved.

Another tasty recipe that is great any time of the day.

Ingredients

1 tbsp butter (or olive oil)

2 slices of whole grain bread

6 large free-range eggs

½ onion, diced

½ red pepper, diced

50g grated cheddar cheese

2-3 baby tomatoes, chopped into small pieces

Splash of milk

Salt and pepper

Servings – 2

Nutrition Per Serving

Calories: 458

Protein: 29g

Carbs: 32g

Fat: 23g

Cooking Instructions

Step 1

Heat the butter, or olive oil if you prefer, in a medium sized pot over a medium heat. Add the diced peppers and onion and saute for 4-5 mins.

Step 2

Whisk the eggs in a large mixing bowl, along with a splash of milk, and then add to the pot.

Step 3

Stir in the tomatoes, cheese, and season with salt and pepper.

Step 4

Toast the bread while the eggs are cooking, and keep stirring the pot regularly to ensure you don't overcook and the eggs are still a little moist.

Step 5

Serve eggs with the toast, and a little more salt if necessary. Simple as that.

Banana & Berry Smoothie

(Ready in 1-2 mins)

Another super quick shake that's good-to-go in a minute or so.

Most supermarkets stock bags of frozen berries, which contain a mix of raspberries, blackberries and cherries. This shake is jam-packed full of nutrients and full of flavour.

Ingredients	Servings – 2
1 tbsp of oats (gluten free if preferred)	**Nutrition Per Serving**
1 ripe banana	**Calories:** 285
Handful of mixed frozen berries	**Protein:** 5g
200ml almond milk	**Carbs:** 59g
1 tsp honey	**Fat:** 5g
1 tsp ground ginger	
2-3 ice cubes (optional)	

Serving Instructions

Add everything to a blender and blitz for 1 minute until smooth.

Chocolate & Blueberry Smoothie

(Ready in 1-2 mins)

Blueberries are the king of antioxidant foods...so it's always a berry good idea to include these in your diet.

Ingredients

1 scoop of chocolate Vegan Blend protein powder

½ banana

Handful of frozen blueberries

200ml coconut milk

2 tbsp linseed/flaxseed

Handful of mixed seeds

Handful of organic spinach

½ tsp of ground cinnamon

Cup of water

2-3 ice cubes

Servings – 1

Nutrition Per Serving

Calories: 917

Protein: 38g

Carbs: 42g

Fat: 67g

Serving Instructions

Whizz it all together and you've got a super tasty, superfood shake that's full of flavour - and nutrients.

Super Green Smoothie

(Ready in 1-2 mins)

The word on the street is that we humans should be eating 4-5 servings of fruit and vegetables per day.

Tick that box by squeezing them all in at once with this healthy, nutritious shake.

Ingredients

½ pint unsweetened almond or oat milk

1 ripe banana

2 green apples

2 large handfuls spinach

20g chia seeds

½ tsp ground ginger

1 scoop banana protein powder

2-3 ice cubes

Servings – 1

Nutrition Per Serving

Calories: 492

Protein: 29g

Carbs: 74g

Fat: 10g

Serving Instructions

Add all ingredients to a blender, whizz for 59 secs, and pour straight into your shaker bottle.

Banana & Mango Smoothie

(Ready in 1-2 mins)

The great thing about these shakes is that you can prepare them easily at night, put them into the fridge in a shaker bottle, and then grab it on the way out the door to work in the morning.

That means no rushing around trying to cook something up before you leave the house, or grabbing some junk food elsewhere.

Ingredients

1 scoop of banana protein powder

½ banana

½ cup frozen mango chunks

200ml coconut milk

2 tbsp linseed/flaxseed

Handful of almonds

Handful of organic spinach

½ tsp of ground ginger

Servings – 1

Nutrition Per Serving

Calories: 764

Protein: 37g

Carbs: 35g

Fat: 54g

Serving Instructions

As always, add all the ingredients to a blender and whizz together for 60 secs.

Blueberry Chia Smoothie

(Ready in 1-2 mins)

Chia seeds are tiny - but they have big health benefits. That's exactly why we're throwing plenty of them straight into this smoothie.

High in antioxidants, great source of protein, fibre, high in omega-3 fatty acids, and important minerals including calcium and magnesium.

Don't be shy in heaping your tablespoon with these bad boys.

Ingredients

1 scoop of chocolate or banana protein powder

2 tbsp chia seeds

1 ripe banana

100g frozen blueberries

½ tsp ground ginger

300ml water

1 tsp lemon zest

Servings – 1

Nutrition Per Serving

Calories: 437

Protein: 30g

Carbs: 58g

Fat: 9g

Serving Instructions

Add all the ingredients to a blender. Grate in the lemon zest. Blend for 60 secs. The end.

MACRO MEALS (LOW & HIGH CALORIE)

* MEXICAN-STYLE SWEET POTATO HASH - P37

Macro Meals (Low & High Calorie)

Some people like to keep track of their calories, others can't be bothered.

Personally, we think that when you make good food choices consistently and workout regularly, calorie counting becomes unnecessary.

And if you throw intermittent fasting into the mix with a clean diet and hitting the gym regularly, you really can't go wrong.

But if you're keeping those calories in check to lose bodyfat and to try and achieve a weight loss target, then we've provided meals conveniently split into low and higher calorie categories. As always, you can see the breakdown of macronutrients for every single recipe.

Couple of pointers before you hit the kitchen...

#1 - We don't *usually* recommend using a microwave when preparing your meals. Microwave ovens zap the goodness out of your food, and that's why it's always best to cook fresh as much as possible.

However, we make an exception when it comes to rice in a couple of these recipes. Rice can be tricky to get right - sometimes it turns out like one big congealed mess, or it's just not as light and fluffy like your favourite restaurant cooks it.

That's why, if you don't have a rice cooker, it's easier and very convenient to simply use pre-cooked microwave rice bags (which are usually ready in 2 mins).

#2 - Who the hell decided to invent so many onions? White, red (which look purple), yellow (which have a tan-coloured skin and are kinda translucent underneath)...those damn tasty aqua blue onions.

Seriously, when we're talking about onions in the upcoming recipes we're always referring to the 'yellow' onions with the tan-coloured skin that are generally used for cooking.

The only other onions used are red onions and spring onions, and we'll mention those specifically.

And if you ever come across an exotic-looking aqua blue onion, please don't eat it.

What's On The Menu

Hot Cheesy Bean Chilli

Falafel Burgers

Mushroom Parmigiana Bake

Smoky Paprika Potatoes

Zero Beef Chilli

Broccoli, Rice & Cheese Bake

Chilli Rice Bake

Nut Loaf

Veggie Ratatouille

Winter Porridge

Veggie Shepherd's Pie

Chocolate Pavlova

Strawberry Pavlova

Mexican Style Sweet Potato Hash

Kidney Bean Curry

Moroccan Style Sweet Potato & Lentil Soup

Spicy Veggie Protein Soup

Plenty on the menu for you to choose from, and we've split them into lower calorie options first (under 350 calories per serving) and then a selection of higher calorie meals (above 350 calories per serving).

Enough reading, let's get cooking.

Mexican Style Sweet Potato Hash

(Ready in 25-30 mins)

Ingredients

2 medium sweet potatoes, peeled and cut into cubes

2 tbsp olive oil

1 red onion, thinly sliced

2 handfuls of organic spinach

400g can black beans, rinsed

1 red chilli, de-seeded and diced

½ tsp of chilli flakes

½ tsp of ground cumin

1 tsp of sea salt

½ lime

½ cup grated cheddar cheese

Servings — 4

Nutrition Per Serving

Calories: 267

Protein: 12g

Carbs: 33g

Fat: 11g

Cooking Instructions

Step 1

Heat 2 tbsp of olive oil in a large non-stick skillet, and cook the sweet potatoes over a medium-high heat. Stir occasionally for 15-20 mins until the potatoes go brown and soft.

Step 2

Add the red onion, diced chilli, chill flakes, cumin, and salt. Give a thorough stir and then add the black beans. Reduce to a medium heat and cook for another 4-5 mins.

Step 3

Spread 2 handfuls of spinach over the cooking hash mixture and cook until the leaves are wilted. Squeeze the juice of half a lime over the top.

Step 4

Optional (but a good option): sprinkle half a cup of grated cheese over the sweet potato hash, and allow to melt for 1 minute before serving.

Veggie Shepherd's Pie

(Cook time: 50-60 mins)

You don't have to be a shepherd to eat this pie...but feel free to dress up like one at the dinner table.

Ingredients

250g red lentils

2 celery stalks

4 carrots

200g mushrooms

3 garlic cloves, crushed

1 onion

1 tbsp olive oil

1 tsp smoked paprika

1 tsp dried thyme

Sea salt and black pepper

1 tbsp tomato puree

1 tbsp flour (oat, almond or gluten free options are suitable)

300ml vegetable broth

1 can of peas

3 medium potatoes (alternatively sweet potatoes)

Servings – 6

Nutrition Per Serving

Calories: 196

Protein: 8g

Carbs: 32g

Fat: 3g

Cooking instructions

Step 1

Peel and chop the potatoes, and boil them in a pot of water for around 15 mins until softened. Add a little salt to the water while cooking.

Step 2

Rinse and drain the lentils, then cook in boiling water over a medium-high heat for approximately 20 mins.

Step 3

Mince the garlic and dice the onion. Sauté both in the olive oil in a large frying over medium heat for 3-4 mins.

Step 4

Dice the celery, carrots, slice the mushrooms, and add these to the frying pan. Next add the smoked paprika, tomato puree and flour to the frying pan.

Step 5

Add the vegetable broth to the frying pan, stirring well. Season with salt and pepper, and allow the mixture to come to a simmer over the medium heat.

Step 6

Drain the lentils and add to the frying pan, mixing in well. Next, transfer the Shepherd's Pie mixture to a casserole dish.

Step 7

Preheat the oven to 200°c/180°c fan oven/gas mark 6. Pour the vegetable mixture into a casserole dish.

Step 8

Drain the potatoes and mash them well, adding a tbsp of butter. Spread the mashed potatoes over the top of the mixture.

Step 9

Bake the Shepherd's Pie in the oven for 15 mins. For a crispy potato topping, finish off by cooking under the grill for around 3-4 minutes or until golden brown.

Hot Cheesy Bean Chilli

(Ready in 40 mins)

When in doubt about dinner, raid your fridge and cupboards for the ingredients below and cook up this spicy storm.

* Warning: in the event of machine-gun sound effects, it's likely you've overdosed on the beans.

Ingredients

100g dried pipe rigate

2 red chillies, de-seeded and diced

400g can chopped tomatoes

1 tbsp of olive oil

1 onion, diced

50g mozzarella, grated

2 x 400g can mixed beans, drained and rinsed

2 tsp chilli flakes

Handful of fresh parsley, chopped

300ml water

Salt and pepper

Servings – 4

Nutrition Per Serving

Calories: 312

Protein: 14g

Carbs: 44g

Fat: 9g

Cooking Instructions

Step 1

Place a large pot/saucepan on a medium-high heat. Add 1 tbsp of olive oil, 1 diced onion, chillies, and stir well for 1 minute.

Step 2

Add the can of chopped tomatoes, the pasta, 300ml of water, and mix well. Season with salt and pepper to suit your tastes.

Step 3

Bring the pot to the boil and then simmer for another 15-20 mins. Keep stirring regularly to make sure the pasta doesn't stick to the bottom.

Step 4

Keep simmering until pasta is soft. Add more water to the pot if necessary.

Step 5

Remove the pot from the heat, and then add the beans, cheese, chilli flakes, and finally the parsley.

Step 6

Cook at a low heat for 1 more minute, allowing the beans to heat up and for the cheese to melt through. Add more salt and pepper if needed, and then serve.

Smoky Paprika Potatoes

(Ready in 25-30 mins)

Ingredients

700g sweet potato, cubed and slightly boiled

1 onion, chopped

3-4 garlic cloves, minced

1 tbsp olive

2 large red peppers, diced

14 oz can chopped tomatoes
1 tin black beans, drained & rinsed

200g can of sweetcorn

1 tbsp cumin, divided

1 tbsp smoked paprika

Sea salt

100g cheddar

2 spring onion, chopped

½ lime

Handful of chopped coriander

Servings – 6

Nutrition Per Serving

Calories: 263

Protein: 9g

Carbs: 40g

Fat: 9g

Cooking Instructions

Step 1

Add oil to a large frying pan, swirl to coat. Add sweet potatoes, ½ tbsp cumin, ½ tsp salt and cook for 5 minutes.

Step 2

Add onion, garlic, pepper and cook for another 3 minutes, stir occasionally.

Step 3

Add black beans, corn, diced tomatoes, remaining ½ tbsp cumin and ¼ tsp salt, smoked paprika and pepper; then stir. Bring to a boil, reduce heat to low, cover and cook for 15 minutes or until potatoes are soft.

Step 4

Turn off heat. Add spring onion, coriander, lime juice and stir. Sprinkle with cheese, cover and let stand until cheese has melted.

Step 5

Serve hot with plain yoghurt and salsa if desired.

Chilli Rice Bake

(Ready in 35-40 mins)

We've put this recipe side-by-side with the previous one because they're similar...but not quite the same.

This veggie baked dish has more of a kick to it, and is higher in protein thanks to the eggs.

Ingredients

1 red onion, chopped

1 tbsp olive oil

4-5 broccoli florets

4 large free-range eggs

400g can chopped tomatoes

250g cooked basmati rice

1 red chilli, diced

3 garlic cloves, crushed

1 tsp ground ginger

Small bunch of fresh coriander, chopped
Small bunch of fresh mint, chopped
200g grated cheddar cheese (or vegan alternative)

Salt and pepper

Green salad bag

Servings – 4

Nutrition Per Serving

Calories: 318

Protein: 16g

Carbs: 20g

Fat: 17g

Cooking Instructions

Step 1

First preheat the oven to 200°c/180°c fan oven/gas mark 6. Brush a casserole dish with olive oil.

Step 2

Add the broccoli florets to a small pot of water over a medium-high heat and bring to the boil, before reducing the heat and allowing the broccoli to simmer for 5-6 mins until soft. (Cooking them using a vegetable steamer is an even better option if you own one).

Step 3

Drain the broccoli and chop into smaller chunks. Add those to casserole dish, along with the onion, chilli, tomatoes, and cooked rice. Season with salt and pepper and give everything a good mix in the dish.

Step 4

Beat the eggs in a bowl and mix in the garlic, coriander, mint, ground ginger, and some salt and pepper.

Step 5

Pour the egg mixture over the vegetables and rice. Sprinkle over the grated cheese over the top.

Step 6

Bake for 25 mins before serving, along with a green salad.

Veggie Ratatouille

(Ready in 65 mins)

Ingredients

1 tsp olive oil

1 tsp apple cider vinegar

3 garlic cloves – minced

1 courgette

1 aubergine

Handful of fresh basil

1 tbsp oregano

1 can of tomatoes and herbs

¼ teaspoon chilli powder

1 red onion

1 tbsp tomato puree

4 large plum tomatoes

Salt and pepper

Servings – 2

Nutrition Per Serving

Calories: 206

Protein: 7g

Carbs: 23g

Fat: 9g

Cooking Instructions

Step 1

In a large mixing bowl, combine the canned tomatoes, vinegar, oil, oregano, basil, chilli powder, salt and pepper.

Step 2

Preheat oven to 180°c/160°c fan oven/gas mark 4.

Step 3

Transfer to mixture to a lightly-greased oven proof dish.

Step 4

Slice the tomato, aubergine and courgette then place in rows on top of the mixture.

Step 5

Bake for around an hour, then serve.

Moroccan Style Sweet Potato and Lentil Soup

(Ready in 45-50 mins)

The last two dishes in this section are our favourite soups. Packed full of flavour, and each of them contain lentils for a nice injection of protein alongside the quality carbs from vegetables, and the spices.

Ingredients

3 tbsp olive oil

250g red lentils, rinsed

2 litres of vegetable stock

2 onions, diced

2 carrots, diced

2 medium sweet potatoes, diced

1 can chopped tomatoes

4 garlic cloves, minced

2 tsp ground cumin

2 tsp paprika

1 tsp turmeric

1 tsp ground cinnamon

1 tsp ground ginger

Servings – 6

Nutrition Per Serving

Calories: 221

Protein: 7g

Carbs: 33g

Fat: 7g

Handful of fresh coriander, chopped

Salt and pepper

Cooking instructions

Step 1

Pour 3 tbsp of olive oil into a large pot over a medium heat. Add the carrot and onion, and saute for 5 mins, stirring frequently.

Step 2

Add the garlic, coriander, ginger, cumin, paprika, turmeric and cinnamon. Mix everything well and saute for another 1-2 mins.

Step 3

Prepare 2 litres of vegetable stock and pour this into the pot, which means you'll need 4 vegetable stock cubes. (Rule of thumb: 1 stock cube = 500ml of stock).

Step 4

Rinse the lentils well and then add to the pot, along with the sweet potato and chopped tomatoes. Season the soup with salt and pepper.

Step 5

Bring the soup to a boil and then reduce heat to a low-medium heat. Cook for another 30 mins and stir frequently to make sure the lentils aren't sticking the bottom of the pot.

Step 6

Add some more vegetable stock if the soup is too thick for your liking....then serve.

Spicy Veggie Protein Soup

(Ready in 50-55 mins)

Protein from lentils and yoghurt – check.

Top quality carbs from root vegetables – check.

A spicy kick for your tastebuds with chilli and cumin – check, check.

Ingredients

1 tbsp olive oil

1 small onion

1 red chilli, chopped

150g red lentils

3 cloves crushed garlic

400g swede, chopped

300g carrots, chopped

200g parsnips, chopped

2 tsp cumin

1 litre vegetable stock

100g plain yoghurt

Salt and pepper

Servings – 4

Nutrition Per Serving

Calories: 246

Protein: 9g

Carbs: 36g

Fat: 7g

Cooking Instructions

Step 1

Prepare 1 litre of vegetable stock by simply put two stock cubes into a measuring jug and fill with boiling water.

Step 2

Rinse and drain the lentils, the put aside. Next, peel and chop the carrots, swede and parsnips.

Step 3

In a large pot, add the root vegetables, vegetable stock, lentils, and season with salt and pepper. Bring to the boil and then leave to simmer for around 30 minutes.

Step 4

While the soup is cooking, heat the olive oil in a separate small pot. Add the onions and fry for 4-5 mins, adding the chilli and cumin for final 2 mins.

Step 5

Transfer the onions and chill to the soup pot and stir well.

Step 6

Blitz the soup with a handheld blender until smooth (be careful to avoid some nasty hot splashes of soup in your eyeballs!)

Step 7

Add the Greek yoghurt last and stir well. Ladle up – and enjoy.

Chocolate Pavlova

(Ready in 2-3 mins)

Confession time...this actually *isn't* the meringue-based dessert named after the Russian ballerina Anna Pavlova.

There are no meringues, we're not wearing our ballerina slippers, and this is technically not a dessert.

But it does look and taste like a dessert - just a healthier version. So, this is one awesome sweet dish you can enjoy without guilt tripping yourself afterwards.

Ingredients

200g 0% Fage Greek Yoghurt

1 scoop chocolate protein powder

(MyProtein Vegan Blend)

50g Frozen Blueberries

½ medium banana

30g cashews, chopped

½ tsp cinnamon

Servings – 1

Nutrition Per Serving

Calories: 450

Protein: 49g

Carbs: 34g

Fat: 15g

* (Exclude cashews for a low calorie version: 280 cals; 44g protein; 25g carbs; 1g fat)

Serving Instructions

Step 1

Mix Greek yoghurt and protein powder in a bowl – you may need to add a splash of water/milk depending on consistency.

Step 2

Chop cashews into small pieces and add to the bowl. Mix in the cinnamon and stir well.

Step 3

Add blueberries – defrosted or frozen. Chop banana into bite-sized pieces, add to bowl.

Step 4

Mix ingredients well, and eat immediately or store for up to 24 hours in the refrigerator.

Strawberry Pavlova

(Ready in 2-3 mins)

Victoria loves 'Pavlova' so much (aka eats it virtually every day) that she had to come up with a variation on the previous recipe.

How to do that? Easy...swap the protein powder flavour and change up a few key ingredients.

So quick and easy, and so, so tasty. Try not to become addicted.

Ingredients

200g 0% Fage Greek Yoghurt

1 scoop strawberry protein powder

(MyProtein Vegan Blend)

50g fresh strawberries

½ medium banana

15g raw almonds

1 tbsp linseed/flaxseed

½ tsp ground ginger

Servings – 1

Nutrition Per Serving

Calories: 450

Protein: 49g

Carbs: 34g

Fat: 15g

* (Exclude almonds & linseed for a low calorie version: 250 cals; 43g protein; 16g carbs; 1g fat)

Serving Instructions

Step 1

Mix Greek yoghurt and protein powder in a bowl – you may need to add a splash of water/milk depending on consistency.

Step 2

Add the strawberries, linseed, almonds, and ginger to the bowl, then mix well.

Step 3

Chop banana into thin slices or bite-sized pieces, add to bowl.

Step 4

Mix ingredients well and then serve. * (Put bowl in freezer for 10 mins for an even better chilled version).

Falafel Burgers

(Ready in 20 mins)

What would you prefer: a greasy hamburger that rots in your stomach for 186.5 hours - or a food with one of the best names ever?

'Falafel' - c'mon, how cool is that word?

Ingredients

400g can chickpeas, drained and rinsed

1 red onion, diced

2 garlic cloves, crushed

1 tsp ground cumin

1 tsp ground coriander

1 tsp chilli powder

Handful of fresh parsley

2 tbsp plain flour

2 tbsp olive oil

4 toasted pitta breads

Small tub tomato salsa, to serve

Green salad, to serve

Servings – 4

Nutrition Per Serving

Calories: 360

Protein: 12g

Carbs: 50g

Fat: 10g

Cooking Instructions

Step 1

Rinse the chickpeas in a colander, and then pat dry with kitchen roll or a tea towel.

Step 2

Add the chickpeas to a food processor, along with the diced red onion, crushed garlic cloves, handful of fresh parsley, cumin, ground coriander, chilli powder, plain flour, and sprinkle in some salt.

Step 3

Blend the ingredients for 30-60 secs until fairly smooth, and then shape the mixture into four patties with your hands.

Step 4

Heat 2 tbsp of olive oil in a non-stick frying pan, add the four patty burgers, and then cook for 3-4 mins on each side.

Step 5

While the burgers are cooking, turn the oven on to 200c/180c fan/gas mark 6. Add a splash of water to the pitta breads and cook in the oven for a few mins until toasted. Serve the patties in pitta bread – burger style - along with a side of tomato salsa and green salad.

Mushroom Parmigiana Bake

(Ready in 30-35 mins)

Okay, let's bring an Italian flavour into your kitchen...but we'll leave the meatballs and lasagne in Italy.

This is a fantastic alternative dish that you'll love and want to cook again...and again.

Ingredients

1 large aubergine, sliced

200g mushrooms, sliced

1 red onion, sliced

1 tbsp olive oil

100g mozzarella, sliced

400g jar of tomato and basil pasta sauce

1 tbsp of fresh breadcrumbs

½ tbsp of grated Parmesan

Servings – 2

Nutrition Per Serving

Calories: 395

Protein: 18g

Carbs: 29g

Fat: 49g

Cooking Instructions

Step 1

Heat a large non-stick frying pan over a medium heat, and add 1 tbsp of olive oil. Put the aubergine slices in the pan and cook for 2-3 mins on each side until slightly browned.

Step 2

Turn the oven on at a temperature of 200°c/180°c fan oven/gas mark 6, and then place half of the softened aubergine into a casserole dish.

Step 3

Layer half of the sliced mushrooms and half of the red onion on top of the aubergine, and then season with a little salt. Pour half of the jar of tomato and basil sauce over the top.

Step 4

Repeat the layers, and then cover the top with mozzarella slices.

Step 5

Mix together a heaped tbsp of fresh breadcrumbs with ½ tbsp of grated Parmesan, and then scatter over the top of the dish. Bake in the oven for 20-25 mins.

Zero Beef Chilli

(Ready in 30 mins)

Ingredients

3 tbsp olive oil

2 sweet potatoes, diced

2 carrots, diced

1 onion, diced

1 red chilli, de-seeded and diced

1 celery stick, chopped into chunks

1 red pepper, chopped into chunks

2 x 400g cans of chopped tomatoes

2 x 400g cans of kidney beans, drained

3 garlic cloves, crushed

1 tbsp tomato puree

1 tsp dried oregano

1 tsp chilli powder

2 tsp smoked paprika

2 tsp ground cumin

200g pack of microwave white rice

Servings – 4

Nutrition Per Serving

Calories: 382

Protein: 15g

Carbs: 52g

Fat: 12g

Cooking Instructions

Step 1

Heat oven to 200°c/180°c fan oven/gas mark 6. Place the diced sweet potatoes in a roasting tin and drizzle them with 2 tbsp of olive oil. Sprinkle over 1 tsp of ground cumin, 1 tsp of smoked paprika, and season with salt and pepper. Give everything a good mix with your hands and then roast for 25 mins.

Step 2

Add 1 tbsp of olive oil to a large saucepan and heat at medium on the cooker. Add the onion, celery and carrots and cook for 10 minutes, stirring frequently until they soften. Crush the garlic cloves directly into the pan, add the tomato puree and remaining spices. Mix everything well and cook for another 2-3 mins.

Step 3

Half fill the kettle with water and boil. Meanwhile, add the chopped tomatoes, kidney beans, and chopped red pepper to the saucepan. Then pour in 200ml of the boiling water.

Step 4

Add the cooked sweet potatoes to the saucepan and mix everything well together. Taste and then add more salt and pepper if necessary.

Step 5

Heat the rice in the microwave for 2 mins and serve with the chilli.

Broccoli, Rice and Cheese Bake

(Ready in 30 mins)

Ingredients

2 tbsp olive oil

1 onion

3 cloves garlic, minced

20 broccoli florets

100g cooked brown rice

(microwave pack is suitable)

4 tbsp plain yoghurt

30g cheddar, grated

1 tsp cumin

½ tsp paprika

Sea salt and pepper

Fresh parsley, for garnishing

Servings – 2

Nutrition Per Serving

Calories: 418

Protein: 20g

Carbs: 58g

Fat: 14g

Cooking Instructions

Step 1

Heat the oven to 200°c/180°c fan oven/gas mark 6.

Step 2

In a frying pan, add 1 tbsp olive oil. Add onion and garlic, cook for around 2 minutes. Add salt and pepper.

Step 3

Add broccoli florets and 1 tsp water, reduce heat and cook for a further 2 minutes.

Step 4

Add cooked brown rice and stir thoroughly until well mixed heated. Remove from heat.

Step 5

In a large bowl, stir together yoghurt, cumin, and 1 tbsp olive oil.

Step 6

Add broccoli-rice mixture to the bowl and toss to combine. Transfer to a casserole dish and top with grated cheese.

Step 7

Bake until heated through and cheese starts to brown, about 15 minutes.

Step 8

Cool slightly before serving. Add a little more black pepper, if desired. Garnish with fresh parsley.

Nut Loaf

(Ready in 60-70 mins)

If you're as nuts as us about almonds and cashews...then let's all start baking nut loaves...like the nutcases we are.

Ingredients

40g cashews

40g almonds

20g peanuts

5 slices wholemeal bread

(broken up into breadcrumbs)

1 large onion

3 tbsp olive oil

2 large free-range eggs

4 cloves garlic

75ml vegetable broth

150g cheddar cheese

1 tsp dried thyme

1 tsp dried oregano

Sea salt and black pepper

Servings – 6

Nutrition Per Serving

Calories: 367

Protein: 15g

Carbs: 22g

Fat: 25g

Cooking Instructions

Step 1

Preheat the oven to 180°c/160°c fan/gas mark 4.

Step 2

Crush or grind the nuts (you can use a food processor to save time), and then add these to a large mixing bowl along with the breadcrumbs.

Step 3

Dice then fry the onion in the olive oil, using a pan over a medium heat. Cook for 3-4 mins until onion is softened.

Step 4

Add the cooked onion to the large bowl, along with the eggs, crushed garlic, salt, pepper, broth, herbs and grated cheese.

Step 5

Mix all the ingredients thoroughly and then knead the mixture well.

Step 6

Let it stand for 15 minutes, then roll into a roll shape.

Step 7

Place in baking tray or loaf tin, and cook for 45 minutes in the oven. After removing from the oven, allow to cool for 10 mins, then slice up for serving.

Winter Porridge

(Ready in 10-12 mins)

Are you allowed to call a dish 'winter porridge' just because you like to eat it when it's cold outside?

Who cares? We love this simple recipe, and eat it all seasons these days.

You might think that this should be in the breakfasts section, but we placed it here instead because this is a brilliant, filling meal that you could – and should – eat any time. And also because we're crazy cookery rebels.

Ingredients

60g oats

½ ripe banana

1 tbsp peanut butter

1 cup almond milk / A2 milk

1 tsp ground cinnamon

1 tsp honey

Servings – 1

Nutrition Per Serving

Calories: 451

Protein: 13g

Carbs: 65g

Fat: 13g

Cooking Instructions

Step 1

Place a saucepan on the hob at medium heat, and mash the ripe banana into the saucepan with a fork until it's in a gooey, smooth consistency.

Step 2

Add the cup of oats and almond milk or A2 milk. Keep cooking at a medium temperature and stir regularly for 6-7 mins until the oats are soft and cooked through.

Step 3

Add more milk if necessary, and then add the peanut butter, cinnamon, and honey. Stir well for another 1-2 mins to properly mix the peanut butter before serving.

Kidney Bean Curry

(Ready in 20-25 mins)

Ingredients

1 can kidney beans

2 tbsp olive oil, thinly sliced

2 small red onions

2 garlic cloves

1 can chopped tomatoes and herbs

1 tbsp cumin

1 tbsp paprika

1 tsp turmeric

1 tsp ginger

2 tbs garlic granules

Handful of fresh coriander

200g pre-cooked basmati rice

Sea salt and black pepper

½ lime

Servings – 2

Nutrition Per Serving

Calories: 428

Protein: 14g

Carbs: 58g

Fat: 16g

Cooking Instructions

Step 1

Heat the oil in a large frying pan over a low-medium heat. Add the onion and a pinch of salt and cook slowly, stirring occasionally, until softened and just starting to colour.

Step 2

Add the garlic, ginger and coriander stalks and cook for a further 2 mins.

Step 3

Add the spices to the pan and cook for another 1 minute, by which point everything should smell aromatic. Tip in the chopped tomatoes and kidney beans in their water, then bring to the boil.

Step 4

Turn down the heat and simmer for 15 mins until the curry is nice and thick. Season to taste, then serve with the basmati rice and the coriander leaves.

POST
WORKOUT
MEALS

* MIXED BEAN BURRITOS - P93

Post-Workout Meals

It's not just the 'what' that's important when it comes to your post-workout nutrition, but also the 'when'.

So, while we're going to serve up some healthy meal ideas that are ideal for after your gym workouts, it's also worth mentioning that if you optimise the timing of those meals you can get better results.

Most gym-goers will grab a protein shake within minutes of finishing their workout, thinking that they're fuelling the fat loss and muscle development process.

Doing this actually hinders it. Instead, if you wait 60-90 mins before you have that post-workout meal it can lead to big fat burning and muscle building benefits.

The downside to ingesting a sugary protein shake, or healthy meal, immediately after your workouts is that it slows down the production of anabolic hormones. When insulin levels rise as a natural result of consuming your post-workout meal, your anabolic hormone levels decrease.

Also, you'll miss out on even more fat burning that continues after you step out of the gym. During your workout, lots of free fatty acids that have been released from your white adipose tissue are still floating around in your bloodstream.

By delaying your post-workout meal, this results in these fatty acids being 'sucked in' by your muscle tissue and liver to be metabolised. By consuming your post-workout meal too soon after training, these fatty acids would instead be re-esterified into triglycerides and would be absorbed back into your fat tissue.

We first learned about this process through sports nutrition expert

Ori Hofmekler. You can learn more about it in his interview with American fitness guru Dr Chad Waterbury titled 'The Truth About Post Workout Nutrition'.

Check it out by visiting: http://chadwaterbury.com/the-truth-about-post-workout-nutrition/

Now we've covered the when of post-workout nutrition, let's look at the 'what'. If we hit the gym in the morning, we'll usually have one of the superfood smoothies we described earlier 60-90 mins afterwards.

But in the evening, we'll generally have any of the 10 following meals. Forget about the exact number of calories, or the perfect ratio of protein:carbs:fat. The most important thing is to have a good balanced meal made up of *high-quality sources* of protein, carbs and fat.

As Marc tells all fitness coaching clients: "Ain't no point in complicating the uncomplicated."

Give your body the right tools after your hard work in the gym, and it'll do the rest in sculpting a leaner, stronger physique.

What's On The Menu

Veggie Frittata

Protein Wraps

Quinoa Fritters

Spicy Chickpea Burgers

Sweet Potato & Chickpea Curry

Super Simple Omelette

Hummus Pitta Pocket

Chickpea & Tomato Eggs

Mixed Bean Mediterranean Salad

Mixed Bean Burritos

Veggie Frittata

(Ready in 25-30 mins)

Ingredients

8 free range eggs

8 cherry tomatoes, quartered

4 mushrooms, sliced

3 spring onions, sliced

1 red pepper, sliced

2 tbsp of sweetcorn

Handful organic spinach

50g cheddar cheese

Salt and pepper

Servings – 2

Nutrition Per Serving

Calories: 453

Protein: 38g

Carbs: 25g

Fat: 28g

Cooking Instructions

Step 1

Preheat the oven to 160°c/140°c fan/gas mark 3, then whisk the eggs in a large mixing bowl.

Step 2

Add all the vegetables and cheese into the large bowl and mix them together well with the eggs using a spoon. Add salt and pepper to season.

Step 3

Pour the mixture into an ovenproof dish and spread some more grated cheese over the top.

Step 4

Bake in the oven for 20-25 minutes.

Protein Wraps

(Ready in 5 mins)

Ingredients

2 whole wheat tortillas

100g (½ pot) hummus

1 red pepper

½ red onion

Handful of spinach

50g reduced fat cream cheese

Servings – 2

Nutrition Per Serving

Calories: 241

Protein: 15g

Carbs: 41g

Fat: 8g

Serving Instructions

Step 1

Spread the cream cheese over the tortillas, then spread the hummus on top of the cream cheese.

Step 2

Thinly slice pepper and onion.

Step 3

Top with the red pepper, onion, and spinach leaves.

Step 4

Roll up and slice into bite-sized serving pieces.

Quinoa Fritters

(Ready in 20 mins)

Ingredients

1 tbsp olive oil

3 cups of quinoa, cooked

large free range eggs

Handful of chopped coriander

1 small red onion, diced

½ red pepper, diced

4 cloves garlic, minced

1 cup of breadcrumbs

1 carrot finely chopped

½ courgette, finely chopped

Juice of ½ lemon

Servings – 10 small fritters

Nutrition Per Fritter

Calories: 183

Protein: 8g

Carbs: 20g

Fat: 8g

Cooking Instructions

Step 1

Combine all the ingredients in a large mixing bowl and stir, allow to sit for around 5 minutes to absorb the moisture.

Step 2

If the mixture is to dry, you can add a tsp of water. If the mixture is too wet, then simply add more breadcrumbs. The mixture should be able to make around 10 fritters.

Step 3

Heat the oil in a large frying pan. Place fritters in pan, on a medium heat and cook for around 6-7 minutes. Carefully turn fritters and cook for a further 5-6 minutes.

Step 4

Remove from heat and serve.

Spicy Chickpea Burgers

(Ready in 15 mins)

These are perfectly filling on their own, but are also tasty on a toasted wholemeal bun with a little sweet chilli sauce.

We'll leave that up to you. The macro breakdown below is per burger alone.

Ingredients

1 can chickpeas

½ red onion

½ red pepper

3 tbsp apple cider vinegar

1 tbsp sriracha sauce

2 tbsp natural nut butter

Handful of coriander, chopped

2 tsp cumin

2 tsp garlic powder

2 tsp black pepper

½ tsp sea salt

60g oats

2 tbsp olive oil

Servings – 6

Nutrition Per Serving

Calories: 227

Protein: 9g

Carbs: 16g

Fat: 13g

Cooking Instructions

Step 1

Drain and rinse chickpeas, transfer to a large bowl and mash.

Dice the onion and pepper and add to the bowl.

Step 2

Add all the other ingredients to the bowl. Use your hands to mix

very well.

Step 3

Form the mixture into six burgers.

Step 4

Fry the burgers in a pan with some oil at medium heat for 5-6

minutes a side.

Step 5

Serve burgers (and any remaining mixture can be stored freshly

in the fridge for 24 hours).

Super Simple Omelette

(Ready in 10 mins)

This really is super simple to make, and the best part is that you can serve it up in 10 mins.

The eggs and cheese will combine to deliver a protein punch of around 30g, which is ideal post-workout.

A slice of wholegrain toast with butter is a good option for some additional carbs and fats to support your workout recovery. Don't believe the lies – carbs ain't all bad.

Ingredients	Servings – 1
4 free range eggs	**Nutrition Per Serving**
½ red pepper, diced	**Calories:** 501
½ onion, diced	**Protein:** 35g
Handful organic spinach	**Carbs:** 17g
25g cheddar cheese, grated	**Fat:** 32g
Salt and pepper	
Olive oil	

Cooking Instructions

Step 1

Heat a dash of olive oil in a frying pan at a low-medium heat. First add the pepper and onion and cook for 2-3 mins to soften, before adding the spinach to the pan, allowing it to wilt.

Step 2

Whisk the eggs in a bowl, season well with salt and pepper, and then pour into the frying pan on top of the vegetables.

Step 3

Cook the omelette for 3-4 mins and then sprinkle the grated cheese over the top. The bottom half of the omelette should be cooking through, while the top half is still quite runny.

Step 4

Turn the grill on to a high heat and then place the omelette underneath for 1-2 mins until the top of the omelette cooks through and cheese melts properly. Serve, adding more salt if need be.

Sweet Potato & Chickpea Curry

(Ready in 45 mins)

Ingredients

1 tbsp coconut oil

400g can chickpeas, drained

400g can chopped tomatoes

400 ml coconut milk

2 red chillies, de-seeded and diced

2 garlic cloves, minced

1 red onion, diced

1 tsp ground ginger

1 tsp turmeric powder

1 tsp chilli flakes

1 tsp chilli powder

½ tsp cumin

½ tsp ground coriander

200g white rice

400g chopped tomatoes

2 medium sweet potatoes, peeled and diced

Sea salt and pepper

1 bunch fresh coriander

Servings – 4

Nutrition Per Serving

Calories: 605

Protein: 14g

Carbs: 54g

Fat: 35g

1 lime

1 pack of poppadoms

Cooking Instructions

Step 1

Cut the sweet potatoes into small chunks and cook in boiling water for 15 mins until softened.

Step 2

While the potatoes are cooking, heat the coconut oil in a large pan or wok, then add the onion and cook for a few minutes until softened. Add the garlic, chilli, ginger and spices, along with salt and pepper, then stir well and fry gently for a further couple of minutes.

Step 3

Add in the tomatoes, chickpeas and coconut milk. Stir and turn the curry down to a simmer. Finely chop a small handful of the coriander stems, then stir those in too, before adding the juice of half a lime.

Step 4

Cook the white rice or quinoa as per instructions on the packet.

Step 5

Add the sweet potatoes to the curry mix in the large pan. Cover with a lid for around 20 mins, stirring a couple of times and adding more seasoning and spices depending on your taste.

Step 6

Serve with the boiled rice or quinoa, and scoop that super tasty curry into your mouth via a poppadom or three.

Hummus Pitta Pocket

(Ready in 10 mins)

Ingredients

1 x 6 inch wholemeal pitta bread

100g plain hummus

1/4 diced cucumber

1 red onion

1 medium tomato

¼ cup crumbled feta cheese

½ tsp olive oil

Salt and pepper

Servings – 2

Nutrition Per Serving

Calories: 649

Protein: 20g

Carbs: 64g

Fat: 37g

Serving Instructions

Step 1

In a small bowl, toss vegetables and cheese with oil. Add a pinch of salt and pepper.

Step 2

Cut pitta bread in half, and then spread hummus evenly over each of the halves.

Step 3

Fill pitta halves with the vegetable mixture, and then get stuck right into it.

Chickpea & Tomato Eggs

(Ready in 50 mins)

Ingredients

2 tbsp olive oil

1 onion, sliced

400g can chickpeas, drained

2 x 400g cans plum tomatoes

4 large free range eggs

300g spinach

100g feta, crumbled (optional)

3 garlic cloves, minced

1 tsp cumin

Pinch of cayenne pepper

1 tsp smoked paprika

Salt

Servings – 4

Nutrition Per Serving

Calories: 325

Protein: 20g

Carbs: 23g

Fat: 15g

Cooking Instructions

Step 1

Preheat the oven to 190°C/fan 170°C/gas mark 5.

Step 2

In a large, oven-proof frying pan, heat the oil over a low-medium heat. Add the onion and cook, stirring often, for 15 mins.

Step 3

Add the minced garlic, cumin, paprika and cayenne, cooking for a few seconds before adding the plum tomatoes and their juices. Simmer for about 5 mins, breaking the tomatoes down with the back of the spoon.

Step 4

Add the chickpeas and simmer for 5 mins more. Stir in the spinach, make four hollows in the sauce using the back of a wooden spoon.

Step 5

Crack an egg into each well and carefully slide the pan into the oven. Bake until the eggs are just set, about 8 mins. Scatter with feta cheese (optional) and serve.

Mixed Bean Mediterranean Salad

(Ready in 5-6 mins)

Plenty flavour in this simple recipe that is done by hand, and no need for any cooking.

Ingredients

1 can kidney beans, drained and rinsed

1 can black beans

1 red onion, sliced

1 red pepper, sliced

1 yellow pepper, sliced

14 baby tomatoes, chopped

½ cucumber, sliced

5 ounces feta cheese, cubed

½ cup kalamata olives, pitted

1 tsp dried oregano

1 tsp dried basil

1 tbsp dried garlic/garlic granules

2 tbsp olive oil

Juice of ½ lemon

1 tsp balsamic vinegar

Servings – 4

Nutrition Per Serving

Calories: 387

Protein: 15g

Carbs: 33g

Fat: 21g

Serving instructions

Step 1

Rinse In a large bowl, place all the pepper, onion, cucumber, olives and feta cheese, toss to combine.

Step 2

In a smaller bowl, mix lemon juice, olive oil, balsamic vinegar, oregano, basil and garlic.

Step 3

Pour this mixed dressing over the salad mix and toss to combine the mixture

Step 4

You can enjoy immediately, but it's a little more tasty if you refrigerate 45 mins.

Mixed Bean Burritos

(Ready in 20 mins)

Ingredients

1 can mixed beans, drained and rinsed

1 tbsp olive oil

2 red onions, sliced

2 red peppers, sliced

1 cup cooked brown rice

1 pack fajita seasoning mix

1-2 tsp chilli powder (depending on how spicy you like it)

100g grated cheddar cheese (or vegan cheese alternative)

Juice of ½ lime

Salt, to season

6 tortilla wraps

Servings – 6

Nutrition Per Serving

Calories: 308

Protein: 12g

Carbs: 38g

Fat: 12g

Cooking Instructions

Step 1

Heat the olive oil over medium heat in a large skillet, and add the peppers and onions. Cook until vegetables are soft for 5-6 mins.

Step 2

Add the fajita seasoning mix, chilli powder, and then pour in ¼ cup of water. Stir well, before adding the black beans, cooked brown rice, salt and lime juice. Simmer for a few more minutes, then remove from heat.

Step 3

Heat a tortilla wrap in a frying pan over a medium heat for 1-2 mins until it is warm to the touch.

Step 4

Place the tortilla on a chopping board, and place about ¼ cup of cheese down the middle of it. Then place about ½ cup of the bean and vegetable mixture on top.

Step 5

Fold the sides of the burrito inwards, and then fold the bottom over the filling to create a pocket. Roll into a tasty wrap, cut in half, and enjoy.

* Repeat steps 3-5 to make more burritos.

HEALTHY
SNACKS

* RECIPES ARE CAT FRIENDLY

* NO BAKE PROTEIN BALLS - P100

Healthy Snacks

There are tons of different 'healthy bars' out there which seem like the ideal snack in between meals, or energy boost ahead of a gym workout.

Problem is, when you look at the ingredients section you'll find some of them contain around 20g-25g of sugar. This is way too much for a supposedly-healthy snack, especially when you consider that the American Heart Association recommends that women don't exceed 24g of added sugar per day, and men 36g.

Excess sugar in the diet is converted to bodyfat, it weakens the immune system, creates an acidic environment in the body, robs your bones of minerals, and is linked to countless health problems such as type II diabetes and heart disease.

Bottom line: do whatever you can to reduce your sugar intake. You'll reach your fitness goals faster, and you'll be healthier as a result.

Lucky for you, several of the following recipes are perfect tasty alternatives to the super sweet bars sold in health stores. The upside is that these ones contain little sugar, and are simple to make.

What's On The Menu

Tropical Nutty Bars

No Bake Protein Balls

Egg-ceptional Muffins

Crunchy Veg & Hummus Wraps

Brill Banana Bread

Chia Pudding

Cashew Butter & Banana Toast

Chocolate & Peanut Oats

No Bake Protein Cookies

Nutritious Energy Bars

Protein Cinnamon Rolls

Spiced Apple Biscuits

Chocolate Orange Oat Bars

Tropical Nutty Bars

(Ready in 35-40 mins)

Pineapple, nuts, seeds, vanilla, coconut...can life get any more scrumptiously stupendous with ingredients like these?

Nope, didn't think so. These little bars are quick to prepare, and make a handy on-the-go snack.

* Lazy/easy cookery tip: Aldi supermarket sells small 70g Tropical Fruit & Seed Mix boxes. You can use 3 x tubs of these as the main ingredient listed below.

Ingredients

200g dried fruit and seed mix

(or 3 x Aldi Tropical Fruit & Seed Mix tubs)

50g plain cashews

50g desiccated coconut

2 tbsp unsweetened almond butter

1 tsp vanilla extract

Parchment paper for baking tin

For the icing:

3 tbsp coconut oil

1 tbsp maple syrup

Juice of ½ lime

Servings – 6

Nutrition Per Serving

Calories: 255

Protein: 4g

Carbs: 5g

Fat: 16g

Cooking instructions

Step 1

Add the tropical fruit and seed mix to a food processor or blender, along with the cashews, desiccated coconut, vanilla extract, and almond butter. Add a small splash of water, and then blend until a batter is formed. (You may have to scrape the sides and blend again to get enough of the mixture).

Step 2

Add the parchment paper to a shallow baking tin, and then press the batter inside the tin evenly.

Step 3

For the icing: add the coconut oil, maple syrup, and juice of ½ a lime to a food processor blender. Blitz for 30-60 secs.

Step 4

Spread the icing over the batter and place the baking tray in the fridge for 25-30 mins until it sets nicely.

Step 5

Remove from fridge, cut into 6 bars, and serve.

No Bake Protein Balls

(Ready in 35 mins)

These little balls of brilliance are so easy to make as there's no cooker involved.

Simply gather the ingredients, mix them up, and get rollin' into healthy snacks you eat at home - or take with you in a tub to work.

Ingredients

2 scoops chocolate protein powder

100g rolled oats

1 tsp cinnamon

4 tbsp cup smooth nut butter

3 tsp natural honey

1 tsp vanilla extract

30g raisins

50ml milk (dairy free or water)

Servings – 8

Nutrition Per Serving

Calories: 158

Protein: 9g

Carbs: 20g

Fat: 5g

Serving Instructions

Step 1

Add oats, protein powder, and cinnamon to a large bowl.

Step 2

Add in peanut butter, honey and vanilla extract. Stir to combine.

Step 3

Pour in raisins next and stir through. Mixture should be slightly sticky but still crumbly.

Step 4

Slowly add in liquid 1 tablespoon at a time and, using your hands, combine until it comes together in a sticky ball that holds together. If mixture is too dry, add in more liquid but not so much that it won't hold shape.

Step 5

Roll into balls using hands, and then place in a container to set in the fridge for at least 30 mins. After that time, they're good to go!

Egg-ceptional Muffins

(Ready in 30 mins)

Ingredients

3 medium free range eggs

50ml of milk (dairy or dairy free)

½ red pepper

½ red onion

Small handful chopped spinach

Cooking spray

Salt and pepper

Servings – 6

Nutrition Per Muffin

Calories: 41

Protein: 4g

Carbs: 2g

Fat: 2g

Cooking Instructions

Step 1

Whisk eggs, milk, salt and pepper in a large bowl.

Step 2

Dice red onion and red pepper into small cubes.

Step 3

Chop spinach into fine pieces. Add to egg mix and stir through.

Step 4

Heat oven to to 200°c/180°c fan oven/gas mark 6, then lightly spray a muffin tray with fry light.

Step 5

Add mixture to each individual casing, filling only half way.

Step 6

Bake for 20 minutes, then serve up those egg-ceptional little beauties.

Crunchy Veg & Hummus Wraps

(Ready in 3-4 mins)

Snacks aren't supposed to be complicated, and it doesn't get much simpler than this.

Ready to go in a matter of minutes, and each wrap contains good sources of protein, carbs and healthy fats for fuel.

Ingredients	**Servings – 2**
200g tub red pepper hummus (or plain if you prefer)	**Nutrition Per Serving**
2 whole wheat wraps	**Calories:** 360
2 carrots, grated	**Protein:** 8g
1 bag chopped iceberg lettuce	**Carbs:** 43g
Juice of ½ lemon	**Fat:** 19g

Serving Instructions

Step 1

Spread the hummus generously down the middle of each of the wraps.

Step 2

Add a layer of iceberg lettuce and then grated carrot to each wrap.

Step 3

Squeeze a little fresh lemon juice on top to give them a zingy flavour.

Step 4

Roll the wraps up, cut them in half, and then eat.

Brill Banana Bread

(Ready in 40 mins)

Why eat plain old bread when you can have some brilliant banana bread instead?

This ridiculously tasty recipe takes about 40 mins to make overall, but serves up 8 slices of magic that'll do nicely as a healthy snack.

Ingredients

1 cup of coconut flour (or 1 cup of oats ground down to flour)

3 ripe bananas

2 scoops banana protein powder

2 large egg whites

¼ cup almond milk, unsweetened

1 tbsp almond butter

100g walnuts, chopped into small pieces

1 tsp chia seeds

1 tsp of Stevia powder sweetener

1 ½ tsp baking soda

2 tsp ground cinnamon

Servings – 8

Nutrition Per Serving

Calories: 190

Protein: 12g

Carbs: 17g

Fat: 8g

Cooking Instructions

Step 1

Preheat the oven to 180°c/160°c fan oven/gas mark 5, and grab two large mixing bowls.

Step 2

In one bowl, mix all the dry ingredients together: coconut flour or oat flour, protein powder, walnut pieces, chia seeds, Stevia sweetener, baking soda, and cinnamon.

Step 3

Mash up the three ripe bananas with a fork and add to the other bowl. Then add in all the wet ingredients - eggs, almond milk, almond butter – and mix everything together. Use a blender or whisk to mix thoroughly.

Step 4

Add in the dry ingredients and mix them through using a spoon.

Step 5

Spray a 9 inch loaf tin with non-stick cooking spray. Add in the mixture and cook in the oven for 35-40 mins.

Step 6

Allow the loaf to cool and then cut into 8 pieces. Try not to smash the entire banana bread down your throat in one sitting!

Chia Pudding

(Ready in 7-8 mins...and 2 hours refrigerating time)

Ingredients

4 tbsp chia seeds

300ml milk (or dairy free alternative)

1 tbsp honey

1 tbsp Stevia sweetener (optional)

1 tbsp granola

5-6 fresh raspberries

Servings – 1

Nutrition Per Serving

Calories: 454

Protein: 19g

Carbs: 48g

Fat: 21g

Serving Instructions

Step 1

In a bowl, stir together chia seeds, milk, honey and Stevia.

Step 2

Once mixture is well combined, let it sit for 5 minutes.

Step 3

Give the bowl another stir to break up any clumps of chia seeds.

Step 4

Cover and put the mixture in the fridge for 2 hours. Once you remove the chia pudding it should be nice and thick, not watery. If it's not thick enough, just add more chia seeds (about 1 tbsp), stir, and refrigerate for another 30 minutes.

Step 5

Add a layer of granola to the pudding, and then top with the raspberries.

Cashew Butter & Banana Toast

(Ready in 5 mins)

Okay, we're going super simple here...but sometimes you don't have to be a masterchef to serve up tasty food.

And when it comes to a healthy snack, you want something that's quick and easy to make. Three main ingredients + ready in around 3 mins!

* Note, we opt for gluten-free bread as much as possible because too much plain bread can cause gut issues. And cashew butter makes a delicious combo with the banana, but of course you can swap it with another nut butter if you like.

Ingredients

2 slices of wholegrain bread

2 tbsp of cashew butter

1 banana, sliced

Servings – 1

Nutrition Per Serving

Calories: 479

Protein: 13g

Carbs: 69g

Fat: 18g

Serving Instructions

Step 1

Pretty straightforward of course. Slice a banana while the slices of bread are in the toaster or under the grill.

Step 2

Spread a lovely big tablespoon of the cashew butter on each slice of bread, and then top with the sliced banana.

Step 3

Shut your eyes and smile while you munch on that cashew and banana goodness!

Chocolate & Peanut Oats

(Ready in 5 mins)

Ingredients

40g oats

300ml milk (or dairy free alternative)

½ scoop chocolate protein powder

(MyProtein Vegan Blend)

1 tbsp organic natural peanut butter

½ banana (optional)

Servings – 1

Nutrition Per Serving

Calories: 509

Protein: 32g

Carbs: 60g

Fat: 24g

Cooking Instructions

Step 1

Add oats and milk into a bowl and stir to combine.

Step 2

Microwave for 1 minute, then stir and continue to microwave in 30 second increments, stirring between each, until the oatmeal is the consistency you like.

Step 3

Mash the banana and add to the oats.

Step 4

Carefully remove from microwave. Mix the protein powder into the oats, stirring thoroughly until completely dissolved. Finally, top with peanut butter.

No-Bake Protein Cookies

(Ready in 50 mins)

No cooking. No fancy stuff. No messin'.

Let's all be cookie monsters and devour these little beauties.

Ingredients

3 scoops chocolate protein powder

120g oat or almond flour

150ml milk (or dairy free alternative)

3 tbsp coconut oil

50g cacao nibs

1 tsp Stevia sweetener

Servings – 6

Nutrition Per Serving

Calories: 220

Protein: 13g

Carbs: 16g

Fat: 12g

Serving instructions

Step 1

Add the protein powder, milk, and flour to a blender and pulse to combine.

Step 2

Melt the coconut oil and pour into a blender, along with the Stevia sweetener. Whizz for another 30 secs until a dough forms.

Step 3

Add the cacao nibs and pulse briefly until mixed well in the dough.

Step 4

Line a baking tin with cling film or parchment paper. Scoop the dough mixture onto a chopping board/kitchen worktop and separate it, rolling it into four balls.

Step 5

Place each ball on the baking tin and flatten into a round cookie shape.

Step 6

Place the tin into the fridge to set for 45 minutes. Take them out...and try your very best not to smash them all down your throat in one go.

Nutritious Energy Bars

(Ready in 50 mins)

Ingredients

40g chopped pecans

40g chopped walnuts

40g chopped almonds

40g chopped cashews

10 dates finely chopped

1 medium free range egg

2 tbsp cinnamon

1 tsp vanilla extract

Fry light olive oil spray

Servings – 8

Nutrition Per Serving

Calories: 163

Protein: 4g

Carbs: 10g

Fat: 12g

Cooking Instructions

Step 1

Preheat your oven to 180°c/160°c fan oven/gas mark 5.

Step 2

Mix together all of the ingredients in a large bowl.

Step 3

Line a shallow baking tray with aluminum foil or baking paper, spray with olive oil cooking spray.

Step 4

Press the entire mixture into the tray and spread evenly. Bake for 18-20 minutes.

Step 5

Remove tray from oven and allow to cool for 5-10 mins.

Step 6

Pull on the paper or foil to remove the cooked mixture from the pan. Use a knife or pizza cutter to cut into 8 rectangular bars.

Protein Cinnamon Rolls

(Ready in 30-35 mins)

Ingredients

1 scoop chocolate protein powder

200g oat or almond flour

1 ½ tsp Stevia sweetener

2 tsp baking powder

1 tbsp coconut oil

1 tbsp unsweetened apple sauce

1 tsp water

½ tsp ground cinnamon

Light cooking spray

Further 1 tsp Stevia

Servings – 4

Nutrition Per Serving

Calories: 220

Protein: 12g

Carbs: 30g

Fat: 7g

Instructions

Step 1

Mix together protein powder, flour, sweetener, and baking powder in a mixing bowl.

Step 2

Mix in oil and apple sauce until a sticky, soft dough forms. If the end product is too crumbly, mix in 1-2 teaspoons of water until the dough sticks to itself.

Step 3

Using wetted hands, form dough into an 8" x 2" strip on a lightly-floured surface. Then spray the dough strip heavily with cooking spray.

Step 4

Preheat the oven to 180°c/160°c fan/gas mark 5. Then combine the cinnamon and a further 1 tsp of sweetener in a small dish.

Step 5

Sprinkle the cinnamon-sweetener mix evenly over the dough strip.

Step 6

Carefully roll dough strip into a bun shape and place in a ovenproof dish coated with cooking spray.

Step 7

Bake in the oven for 15 minutes. Be careful not to overcook - or it will get tough and hard. Cut into 4 roll slices when you remove from the oven.

Calories (per roll without frosting): 296kcal, Fat: 8.0g, Sat fat: 3.5g, Carbs: 30g, Fiber: 5g, Sugar: 1.5g, Protein: 24g, Sodium: 205mg.

Spiced Apple Biscuits

(Ready in 30-35 mins)

Ingredients

1 cup desiccated coconut

4 tbsp almond flour

1 apple

10 dates

2 tbsp coconut oil

1 tsp ground cinnamon

Fry light olive oil spray

Servings – 6

Nutrition Per Serving

Calories: 226

Protein: 3g

Carbs: 14g

Fat: 17g

Cooking Instructions

Step 1

Preheat oven to 250°c/220°c/gas mark 9

Step 2

Peel and core apple, then place all the ingredients into a food processor until mixed.

Step 3

Cover a baking tray with a baking sheet or aluminum foil and add a few sprays of oil spray.

Step 4

Form 6 round patties and place onto the baking tray. Bake for 20 minutes or until golden brown.

Step 5

Transfer to kitchen worktop and allow to cool for 10 mins before eating.

* These can be stored in the refrigerator or up to 7 days, and are also suitable for freezing.

Chocolate Orange Oat Bars

(8-10 mins...and then 2 hours refrigerating time)

Ingredients

200g rolled oats

30g oat flour

5 scoops chocolate protein powder

40g cacao nibs

3 tsp ground cinnamon

50g of 85% dark chocolate

½ tsp Stevia sweetener powder (optional)

1 orange (zest and juice)

1 glass of water

Servings – 6

Nutrition Per Serving

Calories: 325

Protein: 25g

Carbs: 33g

Fat: 10g

Cooking Instructions

Step 1

Add the oats, protein, cacao nibs and cinnamon to a large bowl and mix.

Step 2

Add the zest and juice of the orange. Add Stevia sweetener (if using).

Step 3

Add small amounts (tbsp at a time) of water and mix until the mixture starts to stick together, but don't make it too wet.

Step 4

Transfer the mix to an ovenproof dish and press it down to make a flat flapjack.

Step 5

Microwave the dark chocolate for 1 minute and then pour the melted chocolate all over the flapjack.

Step 6

Put in the fridge for 2 hours or until the chocolate is set. Then cut into 10 bars and get munching.

Bonus Chapter

Do We Really Need
ALL That Protein?

Do We Really Need ALL That Protein?

The world's gone a bit mental for protein. People who barely exercise are drinking protein shakes these days, you can buy Weetabix 'Protein' in the supermarket, and I'm pretty sure I saw a Protein Mars bar in a shop the other day. C'mon, seriously?

People who do strength training generally end up pretty obsessed by protein. Eggs for breakfast, protein shake straight after training. What goes with it...whether it's wholegrain bread, vegetables, pasta...is usually an after-thought.

But is it really necessary? Do we really need ALL that protein?

Turns out we don't – and it took me the best part of 15 years to realise it. That's why this entire chapter is dedicated to debunking the myth that you need massive amounts of protein to maintain or build muscle. This book costs less than the price of a tub of protein powder and if I'd known years ago what I know now I would have saved a fortune on food and supplements. This chapter alone could save you $$$$ too – and possibly even your health.

I've heard stories of personal trainers telling women to eat 180g, 200g or more of protein per day while doing strength training. These 125lbs women are loading up on eggs, bacon, whey protein shakes...struggling to get through it all each day to hit their protein targets. Then they're surprised when they're bloated, farting like mad, and are constantly constipated. Let's put that kind of protein intake into perspective....

Arnold Schwarzenegger, the world's greatest ever bodybuilder, weighing 220lbs, standing, 6ft 2 ins tall, only consumed around 150g of protein. This was when he was competing for the Mr Olympia title – which he won seven times. Meanwhile, these women are eating MORE protein than him - it doesn't make one bit of sense. We all know that protein builds muscle....but, again, do we really need ALL that protein?

I did a lengthy amount of research on this topic because, let's be honest, there's so much advice out there on diet, nutrition, supplements, macronutrients, micronutrients....that sometimes it makes you just wanna eat pizza and tell the health and fitness world to f**k off. I was really surprised about what I discovered and it appears that some protein myths that have been spouted by 'experts' and the multi-billion dollar protein supplement industry for decades.

You might choke on your protein shake while reading this but what if someone told you that....

- You could probably cut your protein intake by half – and still build and maintain muscle.
- One of the world's most famous bodybuilders only ate 60g of protein per day.
- An athlete who was consuming 300g of protein per day was shocked to discover most of it was going to waste...and he was developing worrying health problems as a result.
- Calories are a bigger factor when it comes to building muscle than you would believe.
- Our bodies can actually recycle amino acids themselves, meaning there is less need for a constant high supply of protein.

When it comes to building muscle and developing a strong, lean physique, the vast majority of experts in the health and fitness industry will tell us: "Eat more protein. Eat more protein...then have another plateful of protein." We're told to simply increase our protein numbers, train hard...and the muscle will come. The standard advice dished out by bodybuilders is: "You need 1g of protein per 1lb of bodyweight."

Some adverts in health and fitness magazines (which get paid megabucks for adverts by protein supplements companies funnily enough...) tell us we need as much as 300g or 400g to build maximum muscle. Maybe it's worth asking who actually came up with these numbers anyway?

This more protein = more muscle idea seems too simplistic. Two very important factors are often ignored/forgotten about...

Protein **absorption** - a healthy digestive system can properly process the foods we eat to provide energy, extract the nutrients to nourish our cells, and help to build and repair muscle. Problem is, a high percentage of people living in the Western world <u>don't</u> have healthy digestive systems due to the processed junk that fills our supermarket shelves.

The fact that the treatment of heartburn, constipation etc is a multi-billion dollar industry in America is proof of this. Many of us also live highly-stressed lives, and in times of stress our digestive system basically shuts down as our bodies go into 'fight or flight' mode. This means we don't break down food as we should - and certainly can't cope with ridiculous amounts of protein in those situations.

Secondly, the protein **source** is also an important factor. There are countless high protein foods we can choose from, but they are not all equal in nourishing the body and building muscle.

For example, steak is one of the highest sources of protein and also contains a good dose of iron and creatine that you won't find in most other foods. It's hugely popular with bodybuilders - but takes up to 72 hours to be properly digested in the body.

It's not unusual for some bodybuilders to eat steak every other day in an attempt to keep building muscle. While the body is still processing the last one, along with other meals in between, it's looking highly likely that we're going to have some backing up of food.

The body struggling to keep up is when digestive problems occur and toxins floating around in the body as a result can also lead to other health issues such as skin problems.

Is All That Extra Protein Going To Waste?

But how can we know for certain either way? How much of all that protein is actually being utilised by the body? <u>Not much</u> – is the answer from Dr Ellington Darden. After carrying out a unique two month-long protein study on himself back in 1970 and finding startling results, Dr Darden insisted that *"the biggest misconception 20 years ago, and still the biggest misconception today"* is the idea that we need huge people lifting weight need a huge amount of protein to build and maintain muscle.

This isn't the opinion of just another "fitness expert". Dr Darden was honoured by the President's Council on Fitness, Sports and Nutrition as one of the top ten health leaders in the United States. Back in 1970, as a competitive athlete and bodybuilder for around 20 years he was consuming 380g of protein per day. Half of this came from protein powder and he was also popping all sorts of nutritional pills to aid his muscle growth.

That was until one of his colleagues, Dr Harold Schendel Professor in the Food and Nutrition Department at Florida State University, told him that was way too much protein and he was wasting his time. Determined to prove he was right, Dr Darden set up a detailed study on his own body.

For two months, he kept precise records of his dietary intake, of energy expenditure, and his general well-being. All his urine was collected and analyzed by a graduate research team in nutrition science.

The results? The study showed his body was excreting large amounts of water soluble vitamins, proteins and other nutrients. As he had been consuming massive doses for years, his liver and kidneys had apparently grown excessively large to handle the influx of all these nutrients.

Why You Need Less Protein Than You Think

If you've been lifting weights for a while I'm guessing you're devouring tons of high protein foods. We work so hard to build the muscle that we want to make sure we make the most gains afterwards. We even watch the clock every day to figure out when to guzzle the next protein shake or have our mid-morning snack. If we don't our gym efforts will go to waste, right?

The idea of reducing our protein intake – even on the advice of hugely respected experts like Dr Ellington Darden – terrifies most weightlifters (aka protein addicts) like you and me. Let's look at some of the main reasons why:

#1 The Fear That Cutting Down On Protein Will Result In Muscle Loss

This is without doubt the biggest worry. The standard advice from the health and fitness industry is more protein = more muscle, and so we keep increasing it as we get bigger and stronger. Here are three examples that completely debunk this theory.

1 – Mike Mentzer was a bodybuilding champion who won the Mr Universe title in 1978 and in 1979 won the heavyweight class of the Mr Olympia competition...both with perfect 300 scores.

Mike's daily protein intake....60g per day. Yes, just 60g per day for a heavyweight competing athlete. Now I know genetics come into play with guys like Mike Mentzer but some weightlifters have his entire daily protein intake for breakfast alone. <u>Mike placed more emphasis on calories than excessive grams of protein.</u>

Before he died in 2001, Mike said: *"Protein requirements depend almost entirely on your bodyweight, not your level of physical activity, because it is not used as fuel as long as the body's energy supply is adequate. The rule of thumb is one gram of protein per day for every two pounds of bodyweight."*

Mike also insisted that buying expensive supplements was a waste of money because we can get what we need from a balanced diet which includes meat, fish or dairy products.

<u>2</u> – Dr Nick Delgado is a nutritional expert who tells us the same thing. He insists we require way less protein than we think – and also maintains that sufficient calories are more important. He follows a vegan diet and only eats around 60g of protein per day. In that case, you might imagine he's a bit of a weakling eh?

Afraid not, Dr Delgado holds a world strength endurance record in the Guinness Book of Records for pressing the most weight overhead in an hour (53,640 pounds!) Dr Delgado says that it's important we take in enough calories, arguing that a protein intake of between 45g and 75g is generous.

<u>3</u> – I mentioned earlier that even Arnold Schwarzenegger consumed around 150g of protein per day (around 0.7g per 1lb of bodyweight). This is still relatively small for a 220lb guy who was training hard for the Mr Olympia world titles. Yet, I don't think anybody could argue with his results.

Also, a study was carried out in 2010 on 8 healthy men, who were each given infusions of amino acids (the building blocks of protein) over three hours. Protein synthesis increased with the influx of more amino acids – but then it began to decrease even though more amino acids were still being given. This suggests that bombarding the body with more protein does not necessarily mean more muscle.

#2 The Worry That It Will Lead To Too Much Weight Loss

Protein is not the body's primary fuel supply, carbohydrates are. By eating a sufficient amount of <u>complex</u> carbs and healthy fats too you can ensure the body's caloric needs are met. This helps maintain an ideal bodyweight, and has a protein sparing effect allowing you to develop muscle through strength training.

For 'hard-gainers' like myself who struggle to add a pound of weight (but can easily lose two or three after a weekend on the booze), it is a good move to focus on increasing healthy fats. Fat contains 9 calories per gram, while protein and carbs contain just 4 grams each. On your shopping list add more nut butters, coconut milk, coconut oil, butter, olive oil, avocados etc.

#3 The Fear Of Gaining Too Much Weight

The complete opposite to the worry above, but a genuine fear for people who have slimmed down by following a high protein diet and by training hard. Our bodies are all different in terms of composition, metabolism, how well we process some foods etc. BUT – if you reduce your excessive protein intake and still stick to a diet that is largely made up of whole foods (i.e. plenty fresh veg and fruit, whole grains, no processed junk) then it's very difficult to go wrong...particularly if you're also lifting heavy.

The Protein Scale For A Weightlifter

Okay, so there are plenty of different opinions about how much protein we need to maintain and build muscle. And we obviously know this varies based on bodyweight. But let's look at the scale based on the information and the people referred to in this article.

- World Health Organisation – 35g.
- Dr Nick Delgado, world strength endurance champion - 45g-75g.
- Mike Mentzer, former Mr Universe and Mr Olympia - 1g of protein per 2lbs of bodyweight.
- Arnold Schwarzenegger - 1g of protein per 2.2lbs of bodyweight.
- Standard bodybuilding community recommendation – 1g of protein per 1lb of bodyweight.
- Advice from some protein supplement companies – 300g-400g per day.

Starting at the bottom end...let's be honest, you would probably eat that much before lunchtime. The World Health Organisation is also giving recommendations for the average person, not someone who lifts weight regularly. Going to the other end of the scale, these figures of 300g-400g are crazy, needless amounts. Dr Ellington Darden's detailed two-month long study clearly showed that large amounts of protein goes to waste.

The standard bodybuilding advice is that we must eat 1g of protein per 1lb of bodyweight. This figure has been around for decades...yet we don't know who made it up and on what basis. Yet two of the finest bodybuilders the world has ever produced are telling us we only need HALF that amount. This advice from Arnie and Mike Mentzer lies slap bang in the middle of the scale and is what I would consider the most sensible.

My recommendation: **1g of protein per 2lbs of bodyweight** is an ideal target to aim for.....but, crucially, supported by a sufficient number of calories from complex carbohydrates and healthy fats.

About The Authors

Marc McLean and Victoria Murphy live together in the Loch Lomond area of Scotland, and share the same love for the gym, weight training, and good food.

Marc is author of the 'Strength Training 101' book series, and is a fitness writer for leading websites Mind Body Green and The Good Men Project.

He is also an online personal trainer, coaching people from all over the world on weight training with his 'Be Your Own PT' programme.

Besides being a brilliant mum, Victoria is a full-time advanced nurse practitioner with a special interest in nutrition and alternative health practices.

Website: www.weighttrainingistheway.com

Facebook: www.facebook.com/weighttrainingistheway

YouTube: www.youtube.com/c/weighttrainingistheway

Printed by Amazon Italia Logistica S.r.l.
Torrazza Piemonte (TO), Italy